£4.55

Printed and published in Great Britain
by D. C. Thomson and Co., Ltd,
185 Fleet Street, London EC4A 2HS.
© D. C. Thomson and Co., Ltd, 1995.
ISBN 0-85116-601 6
E.A.N. 7 780851 166018

People have awkward pets.

What a money spinning scheme.

GEEZER'S ANIMAL ADVICE CLINIC

My dog's too fat, Geezer!

GASP! WHEEZE!

Slim him with a ball to chase — only £5!

£5

WOBBLE

GASP

Seen our ball, Geezer? We kicked it into your garden.

Er . . . no.

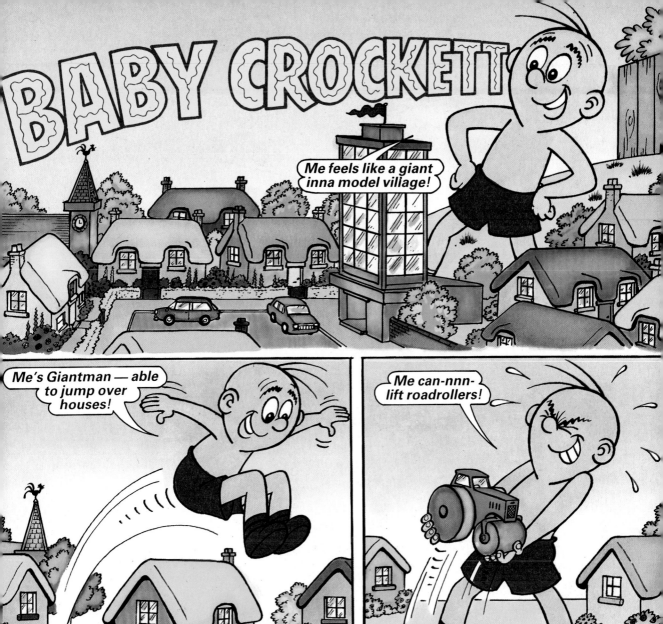

NEWSFLASH!

We interrupt my breakfast — and this annual — with a newsflash. Dateline, brekkie time — and pandemonium in the Crockett household as Baby, sitting in a high chair, decided to rattle his rattle! The rattle was cracked and all the little beads inside that make it go rattle rattle, all fell out and rolled all over the floor — causing Baby's parents to stand on them and fall over . . . In a two hour operation, doctors removed the baby bottle from Mr Crockett's nose. Mrs Crockett's hairdresser is simply appalled at the bacon fat in her hair. Baby's comment, "Funny!".

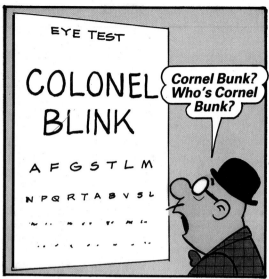

NEWSFLASH!

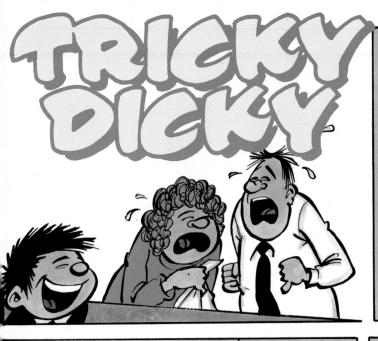

NEWSFLASH!

Dateline lunchtime, newsflash! Workmen restoring an ancient church spire today disturbed a beehive being restored inside the spire by Sting. Several workmen were stung, but nobody seriously hurt. Said Sting, "I was re-roofing the hive when this workman put a hammer through it, cos he missed nailing up a new slate. Well, I was hopping mad so I stung the lot of 'em — you should have seen their faces, worse than the church gargoyles they were!"

WOOARGH!

Don't be scared, readers — it's only me, Baby Crockett, going to the Fancy Dress Contest!

'At's a good disguise. Me can't even tell who's under it!

Come on! Off with the mask so I can see who you are!

Oh, oh! It's not a mask! 'At means it really is a . . .

. . . real monster! HELP!

Bye, Jelly baby! Hope your city's back to normal again!

One thing left to do!

That pollution came from barrels we humans put down here! So I'll put it all back again!

And build a leak proof pyramid to stop it from happening again!

We're home! Back to the Fete!

I saved a penalty!

We saved the Jellymen's city!

END

NEWSFLASH!

Newsflash! Dateline, cuppa time! At the paddling pool today, Geezer tried to rent out hot water bottles. He rented out quite a few, but his bottles caused the ice to melt. An angry mob chased Geezer off. Did he collect all his rental money for the bottles? Said Geezer as he ran, "No. I suppose you could say I just lost my bottle!".

THE BADD LADS

NEWSFLASH!

Er . . . we interrupt this meal with a bulletin. Newsflash, dateline 6 p.m.! Adrian the Barbarian sat down to his evening meal, and said he didn't fancy the Scottish shortbread. The shortbread got annoyed and a fight broke out. Adrian won the battle, as he knew the shortbread would crumble in the end. All the other food cheered on Adrian — except the Spanish omelette. It said, "Don't know why zey are cheering Adrian. He will ze eat us all in a little while!".

ADRIAN'S ARMOURY

Come into my armoury and see some of the strange weapons I keep there.

This is my magic sword — which turns into a feather duster. Very useful for tickling my enemies into surrender!

My helmet has extending horns!

SPROING!

A shield is not only for defence!

My battering ram is self-propelled. In fact, it's a BATTERYing ram!

For scaling castle walls I use scales — the ones on the back of my dragon, Snorrty!

Finally, this is my field hospital — 'cos I don't always win!

NEWSFLASH!